Tom and Ricky
and the
Mystery at Bear Lake

Bob Wright

High Noon Books
Novato, California

Cover Design: Nancy Peach
Illustrations: Herb Heidinger

Glossary: camp, country, island, animals, forest, flashlight, path, mirror, raft

International Standard Book Number: 0-87879-364-X

10 09 08 07 06 05 04 03
15 14 13 12 11 10

Contents

CHAPTER 1

Ricky Has An Idea

It was a hot summer day. Tom and Ricky were at Ricky's house. They didn't have anything to do.

"Boy, it's hot," Ricky said.

"You're not kidding," Tom said.

"What do you want to do?" Ricky asked.

"I don't feel like doing anything. It's too hot. I just want to sit here," Tom answered.

"Let's call Dave and Eddie. Let's see what they're doing," Ricky said.

"They went camping," Tom said.

"Camping? Where?" Ricky asked.

"They went to Bear Lake. They'll be there for a few days," Tom said.

"Camping at Bear Lake. Say, that sounds like fun," Ricky said.

"Do you want to go camping there?" Tom asked.

"Why not? We could go up there for a few days. Maybe we'd see Dave and Eddie," Ricky said.

"That's a big lake, Ricky. They could be anywhere up there. We'd never find them," Tom said.

"Have you ever been there?" Ricky asked.

"No. I've wanted to go," Tom said.

"My dad took me up there last year. We camped out just one night," Ricky said.

"How about it, Ricky? Let's go up there for a few days," Tom said.

Just then Ricky's mother got home from work. "Hi. What are you two up to?" she asked.

"Hi, Mom. We were just talking about camping out at Bear Lake," Ricky said.

"You were?" she said.

"Yes. We won't have to take very much. Just our sleeping bags, a tent, and some food to eat. It won't cost very much," Ricky said.

"And we can catch fish up at the lake," Tom said.

"It's all right with me," she said.

"That's great," Ricky said.

"But you better ask your dad. And, Tom, you better ask your dad, too," she said.

"I'll call dad at work," Ricky said. He went to the phone and talked with his dad. "He says it's all right! Let's go to your house and ask your dad, Tom."

They got on their bikes and rode over to Tom's house. Tom talked to his dad about the idea. His dad said, "I think it will be all right. When will you be going?"

"How about in the morning?" Tom asked Ricky.

"That's fine with me. Let's get back to my house. We can start getting ready," Ricky said.

4

They got on their bikes and went back to Ricky's house. Ricky's dad was home from work.

"Dad, Tom can go. We're going to get all our things ready. We want to go in the morning," Ricky said.

"How are you going to get there? It's not that close," his dad said.

"Can you take us up there? We can hike in when we get there. There aren't any roads going right to the lake," Ricky said.

"Sure, I'll take you up there. Just be ready to leave early," he said.

"Come on, Tom. We have a lot to do," Ricky said.

CHAPTER 2

A Light in the Night

Tom and Ricky spent that night getting ready for their camping trip. Ricky got out his tent. They both got their sleeping bags.

Tom brought some pots and pans from his house. He also brought some food.

Ricky said, "We may not need all that food. Don't forget, we will be fishing, too. We can eat the fish that we catch."

"Let's be safe. We might not catch any fish. This way we'll have enough," Tom said.

6

Early the next morning Ricky's dad drove the boys to Bear Lake.

The lake was about 25 miles from town. It was out in the country. There were lots of trees all around. The lake was about a mile away from the road.

"How will you get to the lake?" Ricky's dad asked.

"We will walk there. We can carry our things," Ricky answered.

"OK. I'll pick you up here Friday morning. See you then," Ricky's dad said.

The boys got out of the car. They picked up their camping things. Then they started to walk into the woods. They followed a path.

"Do you know where we are going to camp?" Tom asked.

"Yes. I think I can find the place I was at a year ago. This path leads to the lake," Ricky answered.

The boys walked and walked. At last, they got to the lake. "There it is! There's Bear Lake!" Ricky said.

The lake was very big. Woods were all around.

Tom looked at the lake. Then he said, "Boy! This is really away from everything!"

"And it looks like we have it all to ourselves," Ricky answered.

"Why is that?" Tom asked.

"There is no road to the lake. That's why not many people come camping here," Ricky answered.

"There it is! There's Bear Lake!"

"Do you think we'll see Dave and Eddie?" Tom asked.

"I don't think so. This place is too big. They could be anywhere," Ricky answered.

Tom saw an island in the lake. "What is that island?" he asked.

"It's called Bear Island. They don't let people go there. The island is only for birds and animals," Ricky answered.

"Let's set up our camp," Tom said.

"OK," Ricky answered.

The boys found a place for their tent. They set it up. They put their sleeping bags inside.

They made a small fire. Then they cooked some food and ate.

Now it was getting dark. The sun was going down.

They talked and then they got ready to go to sleep. Ricky put out the fire. "We have to be safe. We don't want to start a forest fire," he said.

Just then, Tom thought that he saw something. "Look! I just saw a light coming from the island!" he said.

"I don't see anything. Maybe it was just the moon shining on the water," Ricky said.

Everything was dark.

CHAPTER 3

A Strange Noise

"I'm sure that I saw a light come from the island," Tom said.

Ricky answered, "I didn't see anything. Maybe your eyes were playing a trick on you."

"Maybe. But it sure did look like a light," Tom said.

"There is no one around here but us," Ricky said.

"Do you think it could have been Dave and Eddie?" Tom asked.

"No way. They don't let people on that island," Ricky answered.

Ricky put some water on the dead fire. Then they went inside the tent.

The boys went to sleep. The woods around them were dark. The moon had gone down, and there was no light.

It was now very late. The boys were asleep. But then Ricky woke up. He thought that he heard something.

"Tom! Did you hear that? Someone is outside our tent!" he said.

Tom woke up. "What did you say?"

"Someone—or something— is outside our tent," Ricky said.

13

"I didn't hear anything," Tom said.

"I heard something moving outside our tent.
I'm almost sure of it," Ricky said.

Tom shined the flashlight around. But they could not
see anything or anyone.

"Maybe we should get up and take a look around," Tom said. He picked up a flashlight and turned it on.

The two boys came out of the tent. Tom shined the flashlight around. But they could not see anything or anyone.

"Come on. There's nothing here," Ricky said.

The boys went back into the tent. They got back into their sleeping bags. But now they couldn't get back to sleep.

"I think I'm getting sleepy, at last," Tom said.

But just then there was another sound. Something was tapping on the tent.

Both boys sat up. "What's that?" yelled Tom.

"It's just rain. It's the sound of rain on the tent," Ricky said.

Sure enough, it was raining. Soon it began to rain hard. But it was dry inside the tent.

"Good thing we are inside this tent," Ricky said to Tom.

"That's for sure. It's really coming down hard," Tom answered. All of a sudden there was another sound. It sounded like an animal.

"*That* was not rain!" Ricky said.

"What was it?" Tom asked.

"It sounded like a *bear*!" Ricky answered.

CHAPTER 4

A Signal from the Island

"Are there any bears around here?" Tom asked.

"I don't think so. There have not been any bears around here for years," Ricky answered.

"Then why is this place called Bear Lake?" Tom asked.

"It's an old name. There used to be bears around here a long time ago," Ricky said.

"But you said that thing we heard sounded like a bear," Tom said.

"Yes. It *did*," Ricky answered.

The boys had a hard time sleeping that night. The rain kept falling. It kept tapping the outside of their tent.

In the morning the rain stopped.

"Maybe going camping was not such a good idea," Tom said.

"Maybe not. Maybe we should pack up and go home," Ricky answered.

They got up and went outside the tent. Everything was very wet.

"This is no fun. Let's pack up and go," Tom said.

"I don't think we can do that," Ricky said.

"Why not?" Tom asked.

"Look," Ricky said.

Ricky pointed into the woods. "Look over there. We had to cross a little creek to get here. But we had a lot of rain last night. Look at that creek now!" he said.

The creek was much bigger. The boys would not be able to cross it.

"And my dad won't be back. He's going to meet us on Friday," Ricky said.

"What do we do now?" Tom asked.

"We will have to wait for the creek to go down," Ricky answered.

"And what about last night? You said you thought we heard a bear," Tom said.

"Let's not worry about it. Let's go fishing. Maybe we can catch some fish," Ricky said.

The boys washed up. Then they got out their fishing poles. They walked down to the lake.

The morning was warm and sunny. The sky was blue. Soon the boys felt better. They forgot about the bad night they had spent.

"Are you having any luck?" Tom called out.

"No. How about you?" Ricky answered.

"Nothing. Where are all the fish?" Tom asked.

"They must be on the other side of the lake. Come on. Let's go back," Ricky answered.

They were about to leave the lake. But just then Tom saw something. "Look! I just saw a light from the island," he said to Ricky.

This time, Ricky saw the light, too.

"What is it? What does it mean?" Tom asked.

"It looks like something flashing in the sun. I think someone is on the island. Someone is trying to signal us," Ricky said.

"Trying to signal us? Why would anyone want to send a signal?" Tom asked.

"I don't know. But it sure seemed like a signal to me," Ricky answered.

Tom started to say something. But just then there was a loud sound behind them.

CHAPTER 5

Bears Don't Wear Shoes

The boys ran into the woods to hide. They stayed there for a while. Then they came out again. They went back to their camp.

The tent had been pushed down. Their things were all over the place.

"I thought you said that there were no bears around here," Tom said.

Ricky looked all around the tent. "I don't think that it *was* a bear," he said.

"What do you mean?" Tom asked.

"Look. Someone with big shoes was walking around here. We don't wear shoes that big. And bears don't wear shoes at all," Ricky said.

The tent had been pushed down. Their things were all over the place.

"But why would someone push down our tent?" Tom asked.

"I think someone wants us to leave," Ricky answered.

"And make us think that a bear is doing it!" Tom said.

"You're right. Someone wants us to think it's a bear," Ricky answered.

"But why? All we are doing is camping," Tom said.

"Maybe it has to do with the light that we saw on the island," Ricky said.

Tom started to pick up their things. "I don't know why anyone wants us to leave. But I think that we should go," he said.

24

"How can we? We can't cross that creek until it goes down," Ricky answered.

"Well, we had better do *something*. I don't like all of this," Tom answered.

All of a sudden they heard that sound again. It sounded very close this time.

"Let's get out of here!" Tom said.

The two boys ran toward the lake.

"Now what?" Tom asked.

"Let's keep going. We'll go along the side of the lake. We can swim out into the lake if we have to," Ricky answered.

The boys ran along the side of the lake. They heard a loud sound behind them.

"Is it a bear?" Tom asked.

"I'm not sure. It might be a man trying to sound like a bear. But whatever it is, I don't like any of this," Ricky said.

"If only it had not rained last night," Tom said.

"Right. Then we could have crossed that creek. We could have got away from here," Ricky answered.

They kept on running. Then, Ricky saw something ahead of them. "Look over there! A boat!" he yelled to his friend.

They ran over to the boat.

The boat was pulled up by the side of the lake. Ricky jumped in. "Come on!" he said to his friend.

"Whose boat is this?" Tom said, getting in.

"I don't know. Maybe it belongs to the person who is trying to make us think he is a bear," Ricky answered.

"Well, bears don't have boats!" Tom laughed.

"Come on. Let's get this moving," Ricky yelled.

They got the boat moving as fast as they could.

"Where are we going?" Tom asked.

"To the island," Ricky answered.

CHAPTER 6

On The Island

Tom and Ricky slowly moved into the lake. It seemed to take a long time to get to Bear Island. At last, the boys got there. They jumped out of the boat and looked around.

"What are we looking for?" Tom asked.

"I'm not sure. But I think that we will find the answer to the mystery here," Ricky said.

There were lots of trees on the island. The boys could not see anything but the trees. Then Tom found a path.

"Look. This path leads up on the island," Tom said.

"Let's see where it goes," Ricky said.

"OK. But don't go fast. We may have to run back to the boat. We will be safe out on the lake," Tom said.

The boys walked into the woods. The path went up a hill.

"Look! There is an old house at the top of the hill," Ricky said.

"Maybe that's where the light we saw came from," Tom said.

"Yes. The house and the hill are higher than most of the trees," Ricky answered.

The boys went up to the door of the house.

Ricky opened the door and looked in. There was a girl inside. She was tied to a chair. A rag was tied over her mouth.

There was a girl inside. She was tied to a chair.

Tom and Ricky ran inside.

Tom took the rag off the girl's mouth. He also took off the rope that she had been tied with.

"Who are you? Why were you tied up?" Ricky asked the girl.

"My name is Susan White. Two men named Sid and Jake grabbed me and took me here," the girl said.

"Why?" Tom asked.

"My father is very rich. Sid and Jake have sent him a note. They said that my father must pay them a lot of money. If he doesn't, the men will hurt me," Susan said.

"Where are the men now?" Ricky asked.

"Jake went to see if he could make you leave. He was going to make sounds like a bear. He tried it last night, too," Susan said.

"And where is the other man?" Tom asked.

"I don't know. I think Sid is still on the island," Susan answered.

"Then we had better get out of here. Let's get back to the boat!" Tom said.

They ran out of the old house.

On the way to the boat, Susan told them more. "I saw your fire last night. I was not tied up then. When the men weren't looking, I got a flashlight. I tried to signal you," she said.

"I saw your light. But then it stopped," Tom said to her.

"Sid saw what I was doing. He took the flashlight away from me," Susan said.

"But we saw another light this morning. What was that?" Ricky asked.

"I had a mirror. I used the mirror to flash another signal. But Sid saw what I was up to. He took the mirror away. Then he tied me up," Susan said.

CHAPTER 7

Trapped

"Where could Sid be? Jake told him not to leave me alone," Susan said.

"Maybe he is hiding," Tom said.

"Why would he do that?" asked Susan.

All of a sudden Ricky said, "I think I know! Sid must have seen us coming in the boat. He saw us from the house."

"Then why wasn't he waiting for us when we got there? He had lots of time to catch us," Tom said.

"I think that he *has* caught us," Ricky answered.

"What do you mean?" Susan asked.

They all ran down the path. They got to the lake again. But the boat was not there.

Ricky looked out into the lake. "There's the boat. And that must be Sid in it. He is going away!"

Sid saw them. He called out to the boys. "We pushed down your tent. We tried to make you leave. But it didn't work. So Jake let you find our boat to get here. Now you can't leave the island," he yelled.

"You can't just leave us here!" Tom yelled.

"Oh, yes, we can!" Sid yelled back.

"But you said you would let me go if my father gave you the money," Susan yelled.

"Don't worry! Jake and I are going to meet him at your house today. We will pick up the money. Then we will tell your father where you are," Sid yelled back.

"What do we do now?" Susan said.

"We have to get off this island," Ricky answered.

"Maybe we could swim," Tom said.

"No. It's too far. We would never make it," Ricky said.

"Anyway, I can't swim," Susan said.

Now they didn't know what to do. Susan said, "Maybe we should just wait here."

"Why should we wait?" Tom asked.

"My father will pay them the money. And Sid said then he would tell my dad where we were," Susan said.

"By that time, they will be far away from here," Ricky said.

"We have to try to stop them," Tom said.

"But how? There is no way we can get off this island," Susan said.

"I have an idea," Ricky said.

"What is it?" Tom asked.

"Maybe we can build a raft. We can use parts of the old house to make a raft," Ricky said.

"It might work!" Tom said.

"Let's try it!" Susan said.

They ran back to the house. Ricky looked around inside. He found things they could use to make a raft.

Susan found some rope. She said, "They used this rope to tie me up with. There's a lot more, too. We can use the rope to tie the raft together."

Next, they carried the wood down to the lake. It was hard work. But at last, they had enough things to make the raft.

CHAPTER 8

Smokey the Helicopter

When the raft was made, they pushed it into the water. "Do you think it will hold all three of us?" Susan asked.

Tom answered, "I hope so. Let's try it."

They all got on the raft. It held them. Ricky said, "Susan, we don't want you to fall in. You can't swim."

It took a long time to cross the lake. But at last they got to the other side.

"We made it," Tom said.

"We sure did," Ricky said.

"Do you think Sid and Jake are still around?

What time is it?" Susan said.

"Do you think it will hold all three of us?"

"It's almost three o'clock. They must have gone by now. They are going to meet Susan's father to pick up the money," Ricky said.

"Where do you live, Susan?" Tom asked.

"In town. On Oak Street," Susan answered.

"We have to get there before they do. We have to let your father know that you are safe. If we don't, your father will give them the money," Ricky said.

Tom said, "The creek has gone down again. We can cross it now. Let's head for the road. We can stop a car and ask for help."

"That will take too long. There isn't much time. We have to get some help right now!" Ricky answered.

41

"But how can we do that? There is no one around here but us," Susan said.

Then Ricky saw something that gave him an idea. It was on a tree. It said, "PUT OUT ALL FIRES WHEN YOU LEAVE BEAR LAKE." There was a picture of Smokey the Bear on it.

Ricky ran to the boys' camp. He came back holding a can. "This is some oil we used to start our fire last night," he said.

"What are you going to do?" Tom asked.

"I'm going to call a bear for help," Ricky answered.

Ricky went to the raft. He put oil all over it. Then he set the raft on fire and pushed it out onto the lake.

Black smoke rose up into the sky. Ricky said, "They are always looking out for forest fires. They will come here fast when they see that smoke."

He was right. Before they knew it, a helicopter flew over. The helicopter had a picture of Smokey the Bear on it.

Ricky and Tom yelled. The helicopter landed in an open space. They ran over to it. Ricky told the man in the helicopter about Sid and Jake.

"Get in!" the man said to him.

The helicopter took them all back to town. They picked up Sergeant Collins and told him everything. Then they went to Oak Street.

Tom looked out of the helicopter. He said, "Look! Sid and Jake are just leaving Mr. White's house. They got the money!"

Sid and Jake saw the helicopter. They ran for their car. But the helicopter landed in front of them. Then Sergeant Collins jumped out and grabbed the men.

Sid and Jake were surprised to see Susan, Tom, and Ricky. "How did those kids get off the island? How did they get here so fast?" Sid said.

"We got a bear to help us," Tom said.

"Right! Smokey the Bear!" Ricky laughed.